play!

Hello! I'm Fizz!

And... I'm Jake!

I'm Doodles!

Hey, hey, are you ready to play?
It's time to come and play with the Tweenies.
Hey, hey, what do you say?
Come along and play with the Tweenies!

First published in 2000 by BBC Worldwide Ltd, Woodlands, 80 Wood Lane, London, W12 OTT.
Text, design and illustrations © 2000 BBC Worldwide Ltd.
Based on the Tweenies television programme produced by Tell-Tale Productions Ltd for BBC TV.
'BBC' and 'Tweenies' are trademarks of the British Broadcasting Corporation and are used under licence.
Tweenies © BBC 1998. Licensed by BBC Worldwide Ltd.
ISBN 0-563-475153.
Written by Andrea Wickstead and Sarah O'Neill.
Designed by Susan Jackman.
Colour origination by Polestar Digital Watford Ltd, Watford.
Printed and bound by Proost Nv, Turhout, Belgium.
Photography by Christopher Baines, Alan Olley and Bruce Coleman Ltd. Illustrated by Bill Titcombe,
Alan Craddock, Leo Hartas, Emma Holt, Jamie Smith, Alison Carney, David Crossley, Simon Abbott and Lorna Kent.
Thanks to Danny, Hayley, Dominic, Naomi and Lauren who appear in this book.

Tweenie Clock – where will it stop?

If you're happy and you know it
Clap your hands
If you're happy and you know it
Clap your hands
If you're happy and you know it
And you really want to show it
If you're happy and you know it
Clap your hands

If you're happy and you know it
Nod your head
If you're happy and you know it
Nod your head
If you're happy and you know it
And you really want to show it
If you're happy and you know it
Nod your head

4

Teeny Tweenies!

One day, the Tweenies were out exploring by the climbing frame.

"Let's look for a wiggly worm!" said Milo, excitedly, "everyone has to look for a wiggly woo worm!"

So they all started looking for a worm. "If we find it we'll just look at it, we won't touch it because little worms are much happier being left alone," said Bella.

Bella decided to go to the top of the climbing frame to look for a worm.

"There won't be any worms up there, Bella!" cried Milo.

"I know," said Bella, "but from here I'll be able to see the whole garden. I'll be like a bird looking

for a worm," she added.

Bella really did spot a worm – right by Doodles' nose! Milo spotted it too and picked it up.

"MILO! You're not supposed to touch the worm, only look at it!" she said, thinking how scared the poor little worm would be.

"If you were shrunk down as tiny as a worm you wouldn't like it if a big monster picked you up," explained Bella.

Fizz agreed, "I think you would be scared Milo. I dreamt I was shrunk once, so I know..."

"Really?" said Jake. Fizz explained what it had been like when she was tiny and told them that it was a bit scary.

"That's silly, I wouldn't be scared at all," said Milo, folding his arms.

Jake asked how Fizz had shrunk and she told them all how she had said a magic word in her dream, but she couldn't tell them the word or she would shrink!

"Would you really get smaller and smaller and smaller and smaller?" asked Jake. Fizz nodded.

Milo thought shrinking sounded great. "Let's all do it!" he said.

Doodlebug... ...doodlebug... ...doodlebug!

Fizz thought for a while then said, "Okay everybody, we have to hold hands, go round in a circle and say the magic word, 'doodlebug', three times."

And that's just what they did...

"One, two, three! Doodlebug, doodlebug, doodlebug!" they cried as they went round in a circle.

The Tweenies got smaller...

...and smaller...

...and smaller...

...and smaller, until they were no bigger than a tiny mouse!

7

They looked around them. "WOWEE! Are we in the jungle?" said Jake, looking at all the tall grass and trees. Then Milo spotted something – "Look! There's a castle over there," he cried, pointing.

"This jungle is strange," said Bella. But Fizz knew where they were. "This isn't a jungle – we're in the garden," she explained.

"Our garden hasn't got a castle in it," said Jake, looking very confused. Milo decided to get a closer look at the castle. "Follow me," he said, timidly.

When they got to the castle, they tried to guess who lived inside. Jake thought it might be a big monster and got a bit scared.

"I know what this is," said Fizz. "It isn't a fairy castle, it's our bucket from the sandcastle... and

that's our football," she said, pointing to a football as big as a house!

"WOW! I could never kick that!" cried Milo.

"Look at the flowers, they're as big as trees!" cried Bella.

"We really have shrunk!" they all cried, at once.

"It feels funny down here – everything looks enormous," said Bella. She was right – the climbing frame was as big as a mountain!

"HUGEROONY!" cried Milo.

"I think we're only as big as a wiggly worm," said Jake and decided that they should all look for the worm to say hello.

Bella thought it was a great idea. "We're only small now so we won't frighten him," she said.

But Milo wasn't so sure, in fact he was a bit scared. "I'll wait here

while you look for him," he said. But he was even more scared on his own. "Wait for me!" he cried, as the others headed off on their worm hunt.

The teeny Tweenies didn't find the worm, but they did find something else... it was huge... and hairy!

"It's a big hairy mountain!" cried Milo. The mountain started to rumble.

"It might be a volcano," said Bella, taking a step back.

"No, it's a snozzlemonster, a big hairy snozzlemonster – we'll have to fight him!" cried Milo. The others didn't like the idea of fighting.

"We could tickle him," suggested Jake. And that's what they did. The big hairy mound moved and started to come towards them!

"It's Doodles!" cried Jake. "Doodles, it's us – we're down here."

"Oh! Teeny Tweenies!" muttered Doodles and got even closer.

"We've got to get big again, or else he'll squash us!" cried Milo. "Quick let's all say the magic word!"

They all grabbed each other and said the magic word as quickly as they could... "Doodlebug, doodlebug, doodlebug!"

The teeny Tweenies got bigger and bigger and bigger... until they were back to their normal size. "Now that's magic!" said Doodles, looking amazed.

"Hmmm, now I know what it feels like to be a little worm," said Milo, "I'll never scare one again!"

Balloon faces!

felt bow

wool hair
with beads

tissue
paper hair

paper eyes
and mouths

Bella

Fizz

strips
of black
paper
for hair

paper eyes
and mouths

yellow
feather
hair

Jake

Milo

red wool
hair

paper eyes
and mouths

cotton
wool hair

Judy

Max

Tweenie Band!

Oh, we can play in the Tweenie Band
And this is the way we do it...
Shake, bang, ting,
Goes the Tweenie Band...
And that's the way we do it!

Use your favourite colours to make the
Tweenie Band as bright as possible!

Dotman to the rescue!

"More water! More water!" cried Jake, as he carried buckets of water from the sink.

Judy looked very puzzled when she saw him, but Jake explained that he needed the water for pouring.

"I see, well be careful and don't leave the tap running or we'll be flooded out," said Judy.

"I won't," said Jake and got on with his pouring. But then he had a thought... "Did I turn the tap off? I think I did. I put the plug in so that I wouldn't waste any."

Then Jake started imagining what it would be like if the playroom did get flooded...

"The water would pour in and get deeper and deeper, even deeper than in the deep end of the swimming pool. It would fill the playroom. The water would rush around and swirl here and swirl there. It would splash around and pick up Milo in his chair. Doodles would still be asleep on his beanbag as it started to float away and Bella would be stranded on the climbing frame."

Soon the playroom WAS filling up with water!

"Hold on, everybody, I'm coming to rescue you!" cried Jake, jumping onto a squishy shape. "My squishy boat will pick you up and take you to safety."

He paddled along on his squishy boat and rescued Milo and Fizz, who jumped on board, then they heard Bella calling from the climbing frame. "Help! Help! I'm all alone on this island. Is anyone going to rescue me?"

"I'm coming, Bella! Hold on!" cried Jake, paddling away. When they reached the climbing frame, they all hopped off the boat to join Bella.

Jake told them all he was sorry for having left the tap running.

"Oh, where are Max and Judy? They must be too busy to come and rescue us," sighed Bella.

"We need to find a way of getting rid of all this water," said Milo. "The plughole!" cried Jake, suddenly. "The water always runs down the plughole when you take the plug out," he added.

"But the plughole is way over there," sighed Fizz, pointing across the water.

"This is a job for DOTMAN!" cried Jake. "Don't go away. I'll be back!" Dotman flew off towards the plughole.

He rushed into the playroom and dived into the water.

The others waited for him on the climbing frame. "He's taking a long time," sighed Fizz.

"Don't worry! If anyone can find the plug it's Dotman," said Milo.

All of a sudden Dotman flew out of the water holding the plug and chain in his hand.

"Hooray!" cried the others, as the water gurgled away.

"Well done, Dotman!" cried Bella.

"We all love Dotman!" said Fizz.

"Dotman, my hero!" called Milo.

Later, Jake was playing with the water and jug again when Judy walked by.

"Judy!" cried Jake, excitedly. "We were looking for you – the playroom filled up with lots and lots of water! We wanted you to rescue us but we couldn't find you so I rescued everyone instead," he said, proudly.

"Well done, Jake," laughed Judy. "You're a real hero!"

Fizz's rainbow

Fizz and Doodles have spotted a magical rainbow! Use your brightest colours to finish the rainbow – look at the key to find out which colours to use.

Key 1 2 3 4 5 6 7

I'm a little robot

Sing along with the Tweenies to the tune of 'I'm a little teapot.'

I'm a little robot,
Strong and bright,
Here's my button,
Here's my light.
If you wind me up,
You'll see me walk,
Push my buttons,
I will talk!

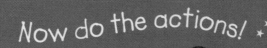

I'm a little robot,
strong and bright,

Stand very still and stiff,
imagine you are very shiny.

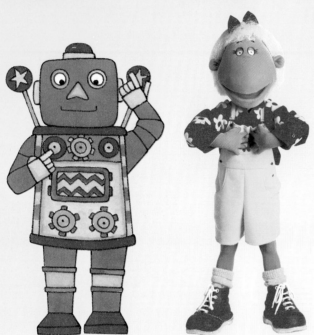

Here's my button,
Here's my light.

Point to your buttons.

If you wind me up,
You'll see me walk,

Walk, keeping your arms
and legs very stiff!

Push my button,
I will talk!

Talk in a robotic voice.
What will you say?

Milo's dragon

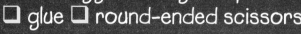

To make Milo's fire-breathing dragon, you will need:
- ☐ a cardboard tube ☐ egg box ☐ green paint ☐ coloured paper
- ☐ glue ☐ round-ended scissors

1

Paint an egg box and a cardboard tube with your bright green paint.

2

Stick a small box to the tube to make a head and fix it onto the body. Now cut out a tail, wings and some scales then glue them into place.

3

Cut out some flames, eyes and ears from coloured paper to add the finishing touches to your dragon!

Your fire-breathing dragon is now ready! Can you think of a name for your dragon?

Make a dragon really appear by colouring all the spaces with dots in them!

21

Fairy magic

Bella's wand is in the bucket behind the spade!

Bella has dropped her wand – can you spot it somewhere in this picture?

Bella has waved her magic wand and lots
of things in the playroom have changed!
Look closely at this picture and see if
you can find the magic changes...

Answers: There is an extra circle on Jake's top, the baked beans are
missing, Fizz has a few beads missing from her hair, Jake's socks are red,
the picture of Milo is missing, there are extra skittles next to Fizz, there
is an extra bucket on the floor and there is an extra shelf on the wall.

Can I live with you?

"This shell is too big and too heavy," moaned Betsy, one afternoon. She had carried her shell from one end of the garden to the other and she was exhausted!

"I need a new home – one that I don't have to carry around on my back," she decided and off she trudged in search of a new home.

A few hours later, she arrived at Wally worm's house. Wally showed her his worm holes and told her how comfy and warm they were to live in.

"Can I live with you?" she asked. Wally nodded and inched off into his worm hole. Betsy followed him, but as she went to squeeze into the tiny hole, she got stuck!

"This silly shell is always getting in the way!" she cried. Wally pushed and puffed as he eased her out of the hole.

"You're too big for my worm holes, Betsy," he said and disappeared back into his hole.

Betsy sighed, but then she spotted a busy ant, carrying a leaf. So she followed him until she reached his home. It was very hard to keep up with the ant, after all, she didn't have as many legs as he did!

"Excuse me," she said. "Can I live with you?"

The ant looked at her and nodded. "I live here – in this ant hill," said the ant, pointing to a big mound of earth with his antennae.

"Now that does look cosy," said Betsy and slid along to the entrance.

She squeezed and she wiggled to get into the small ant hill until...

CRASH! The ant hill came tumbling down around her. Betsy, with her big shell, was much too big for the fragile ant hill.

"Whoops," she said and quietly slid away before the ants could tell her off.

She was looking over her shoulder to make sure the ants weren't chasing her, when she ran straight into something.

"What on earth is this?" she cried, wiping sticky strands out of her eyes. But then a big hairy leg came towards her and she knew...

"Hello, Sid," she said to the spider. Sid smiled, "What are you doing in my web, Betsy?" he laughed.

Betsy told him all about her search for a new home and Sid suggested that she tried out his web for the night.

"Night, night, Sid," she said as she settled down in the web.

That night it rained and the wind blew. Poor Betsy was blown about the web and when she woke up, she was soaking wet and all tangled up in the web!

"I'm sorry Sid, but your web is just too uncomfortable, I'm moving out," moaned Betsy and wiggled off.

"What's that noise?" said Betsy, as she slithered past the flower bed... Buzzzzz buzz, went the noise.

25

Betsy looked up – a stripy bumblebee was busily buzzing about above her head.

"Excuse me, Mrs Bumblebee, can I live with you?" she asked. Mrs Bumblebee, scratched her head. "If you like!" she buzzed and pointed to her house. It was a funny-looking thing, hanging from a branch on a tree. "That's my beehive," she said and buzzed off into it.

Betsy looked at the beehive swinging from the tree as the bees busily buzzed about it.

"Oh dear, that's very high up," she thought as she inched her way up the tree trunk. All of a sudden, her shell felt very heavy and she toppled off the trunk and hit the ground with a bump.

"Ouch!" said Betsy, rubbing her head. "This is no good," she sighed and rested against the tree.

"Are you ok?" asked a long hairy green creature. Betsy rubbed her eyes, "I'm fine thank you."

Then she looked at the caterpillar.

"Where do you live?" she asked.

"Why, I live right here underneath this leaf," said the caterpillar pointing at a big green leaf.

"Hmmm, that looks warm and dry," said Betsy. "Can I live with you?" she asked.

The caterpillar nodded and went to bed – but to Betsy's surprise the caterpillar slept **underneath** the leaf!

She tried and tried to stay under the leaf, but her shell was just too heavy. She kept falling off the leaf and landing on the ground with a bump.

"That's it!" she cried the next day. "I've had enough and I'm absolutely exhausted!" Her cheeks were red with frustration.

"Have you found a new home yet?" Sid the spider asked.

"No I haven't and I'm not going to either," snapped Betsy.

"I've stayed in lots of different homes and I've decided something... my shell house is the best house ever – it keeps me dry, it protects me, it's very warm and it's always nearby!"

With that, Betsy popped her head inside her shell and hung a sign outside – 'DO NOT DISTURB!'

So next time you see a snail in its shell – don't disturb it, it might be Betsy trying to get some sleep!

DO NOT DISTURB

27

Home, sweet home

Animals like to make themselves comfortable in their homes, just like you do. Have a look at these pictures to see how some creatures keep themselves warm and happy. Write over the dotty letters to find out what they are called.

These animals look very snug as they have a nice, long sleep. Their home is called a burrow.

rabbits

dogs

This is Milly and Toby. They share a special basket to rest and sleep in.

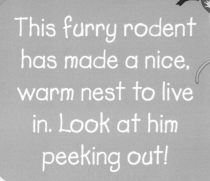

This furry rodent has made a nice, warm nest to live in. Look at him peeking out!

Peek-a-boo!

mouse

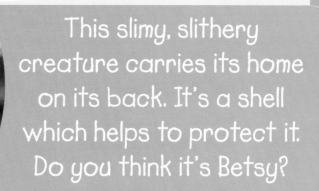

This slimy, slithery creature carries its home on its back. It's a shell which helps to protect it. Do you think it's Betsy?

snail

What a nice, big comfortable cushion this dog has to sleep on. Doesn't he look familiar?

Doodles

Mmmmmmm... comfy!

He's shaggy and baggy,
And not very neat.
He's bumpy and lumpy,
Especially his feet.

He roars and he snores,
And he's dripping with goo.
He grumbles and rumbles...
And he's right behind YOU!

On the move!

CHOO! CHOO!

CHUG! CHUG!

The Tweenies are out and about on the move – where do you think they are going? Colour them in, then tell a story about the pictures.

The Starship Tweenie

"Spaceroony!" cried Milo, one day. "I'd love to go into space and meet lots of little alien spacemen!" Milo giggled and shook his arms, then he spoke in a silly alien voice – "Hello-I-am-a-friendly-alien," he gargled.

Fizz looked dreamy, "Oh I'd love to go and see all the other planets and stars. Space is so beautiful," she sighed.

Jake looked very confused. "Plant it?" he said. "What do you want to plant?"

Fizz shook her head. "No, PLANETS, not plants, Jake. Planets are huge balls which float in space," she explained.

"You know what space is, don't you Jake?" asked Bella.

Jake thought he knew what space was, "When we go shopping, Mum always says we have to look for a space and when we find a space, we put the car in it, but I've never seen any planets in them." He looked very confused, so Judy explained.

She picked up a ball and held it in front of her. "We live on a big planet called Earth, which is like a huge ball. All around this ball is space which goes on and on and on. In all that space there are lots of other planets and millions of stars," she told them.

"I love all the different colours of the planets – red, yellow, blue..." said Bella. Then she had an idea. "Let's make our own solar system of planets," she suggested. So they did! Bella, Milo and Fizz painted some big circles of card and Jake made a rocket from cardboard boxes, tubes and four little yogurt pots!

Bella stood back to admire their work. "We've made our own solar system of planets!" she cried.

"Let's look for aliens!" cried Milo.

Jake whooshed his rocket through the planets. "I'm Captain Jake in the Starship Tweenie..." he cried.

Soon the rocket *was* whizzing through space...

"These are the adventures of Captain Jake and his brave crew as they travel through space looking for new planets, new stars and new people," said a voice. The Tweenies were inside their own big spaceship, exploring outer space!

"Tell me, Mr Milo – where are we now?" asked Captain Jake.

"We are entering a new solar system, Captain," said Milo. Suddenly Fizz saw something – five big planets were floating on a big screen in front of them.

"Look! There are some new planets. They are all different patterns and colours, Captain," cried Fizz.

"That one's checked and that one's all speckly... how strange," said Captain Jake, looking at the planets.

Then Fizz noticed something. "Captain, we are receiving a signal – someone needs help!"

A picture appeared on the big screen – five funny-looking aliens! "Help! Help!" they were saying. "Aliens! Fabaroony!" cried Milo.

"It seems they need help," said Bella. Captain Jake agreed and told Bella to whoosh him down there. He went and stood on a special circle as Bella pushed a button and... he disappeared! A few seconds later he whooshed onto the planet with the aliens.

"Thank goodness you're here," said the spotty alien. "We thought we'd be stuck here forever – our rocket is broken and we have no way of getting home," added the stripy alien.

"Do not fear, Captain Jake is here," said Jake, then he contacted Bella. "Six to whoosh aboard," he said, as they all vanished... and reappeared on board the spaceship.

Back on board, Captain Jake told Fizz to set a return course to the new planets. The speckly planet appeared on the screen.

"That's Planet Speckly, that's where I live," said the speckly alien.

Can you match the aliens to their planets?

The Tweenies sang a song as each alien was whooshed back to its planet...

"Five little men on the Starship Tweenie needed to get back home. We looked left and right for a planet that was right and one man went back home."

"Look! My planet – it matches me!" cried the checked alien as he whooshed back to his planet.

Soon the aliens had all whooshed home to their planets.

"Hmmm, it seems we have successfully returned the aliens to their natural habitat," said Mr Milo.

"Pardon?" said Captain Jake, looking confused.

Bella explained, "He means we did it!" she cried.

"Hooray!" cried the others.

Fizz sighed, "It must be so nice for them to be back home," she said.

"Captain Jake, can I set a return course for *our* home?" asked Bella.

Captain Jake nodded, "Make it so!" he said, as the rocket zoomed home.

Lost in space!

Follow each line with your finger to help the
Tweenies find their way to some new planets!

Doodles has discovered some aliens – one of them is different.
Draw a ring around the odd one out!

Join up the dots to see some strange aliens from another planet!

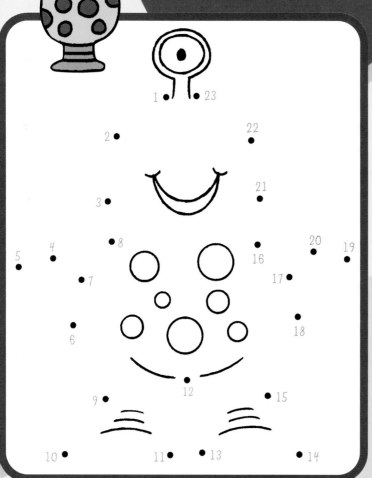

Match up the planets which are the same!

Incy Wincy Spider

Incy Wincy Spider climbed up the water spout,
Out came the rain and washed poor Incy out.
Out came the sun and dried up all the rain,
So Incy Wincy Spider climbed up the spout again.

Now do the actions!

Incy Wincy Spider climbed up the water spout,

(Imagine your hand is the spider, your fingers are the spider's legs and your arm is the spout)

Out came the rain and washed poor Incy out.

(Let your spider whizz down your arm)

Out came the sun and dried up all the rain,

(Make a big circle with your arms to show the sun is shining)

So Incy Wincy Spider climbed up the spout again.

(Make your spider climb up your arm again!)

41

Make Jake's spiders!

To make Jake's springy spiders, you will need:
- ☐ a round piece of coloured paper or card ☐ white paper
- ☐ elastic or cotton ☐ round-ended scissors ☐ sticky tape

Cut into the middle of the circle and overlap the two edges, then stick them together to make a shallow cone shape.

Fold the cone in half, then again and again.

Draw an arrow shape onto the card and cut out around the arrow, just as Hayley is doing!

Open up the card and your spider is almost ready! Just bend the legs at the knees...

Milo's woolly jumper is unravelling.
Colour the picture and add some wool
to the tangled Tweenies!

Caterpillars and ladders

40

finish

39

38

37

25

26

27

28

24

23

22

21

9

10

11

12

8

7

6

5

Play this great up and down game with a friend! Take it in turns to throw a dice and move your counter across the board – buttons make great counters. If you land on a ladder, climb up, but if you land on the end of a caterpillar, down you go!

Milo the clown

Once upon a time, there was a wonderful circus. There was a Ringmaster, with a big top hat called Doodles. There was a beautiful dancer called Fizz and there was the greatest magician in the world – 'the Great Jakendo!'

"Whooosh, kazoom, whooosh!" said Jake as he pulled a rabbit out of his hat.

There was Bella, blowing the horns. "Ladies and gentlemen, be delighted by the beauty of Bella!" cried Doodles, as everyone cheered.

Soon it was time to announce Milo the clown! Everyone loved clowns and the audience couldn't wait to see him. But Milo was very nervous. He had practised and practised at being funny, but no matter how hard he tried he just couldn't get it right.

"And now, ladies and gentlemen, I give you Milo the clown... ahem... Milo the clown," said Doodles. The audience clapped and cheered and waited and waited and waited...

Milo was sitting in his dressing room looking very sad. He tried to juggle the balls and balance plates on a stick, but he just couldn't get it right.

"Oh, it's no good, I can't do any of these clown tricks. What's the use of a clown who can't do any of the things clowns do? My jokes aren't funny and my tricks are terrible. I can't juggle or tumble – the audience will grumble... and I've got no smile." Milo looked sadly into the mirror at his reflection.

Jake went to find Milo. "Everyone is looking for you, Milo. You've got to go and perform your clowny things."

"I'm sorry Jakendo, I can't do my tricks. When I try, they all go wrong. If I juggle balls or spin plates they just fall and break... look!" said Milo, showing Jake his tricks. Jake started to laugh and laugh... and laugh!

"That's the funniest thing I've ever seen," said Jake. Milo thought for a while, then said, "If I do things MY way, maybe I will be funny!" he said, as a smile crept over his face.

Meanwhile, Doodles was trying to keep the audience happy. "Phewee!" he said in relief as Milo appeared. Everyone started to cheer very loudly.

Milo spun the plates and as they fell to the ground the audience laughed more and more. He tried to juggle the balls, but got in a muddle. He got into his clown's car and the doors and wheels fell off. Milo couldn't believe it, people were cheering and laughing – they liked him!

"You're the best clown ever, Milo!" said Jake. And the audience definitely agreed... What do you think of Milo the clown?

Busy big top

The circus has come to town! Look carefully at the picture, then answer the questions below.

One of the clowns is throwing a custard pie. True or false?

What colour is the hoop?

The juggler is juggling five skittles. True or false?

How many hats can you find?

How many glasses is the tightrope walker carrying?

What is in the magician's hat?

Now make up a story about a big top show!

Let's clown around!

Make these great Tweenie clown hats and cakes for your next party.
For the hats you will need: ☐ coloured paper ☐ round-ended scissors
☐ safe glue ☐ coloured stickers ☐ pens ☐ elastic

1 Cut a semi-circle from a piece of colourful card.

2 Roll the paper into a cone shape and glue the edge down.

Clowneroony!

3 Decorate your hat with stickers and coloured pens. Ask a grown-up to attach a piece of elastic to the bottom of the hat.

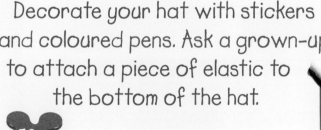

Now you're ready to party like the Tweenies!

Why not make some clown cakes for your party? Simply decorate some fairy cakes with icing sugar, icing pens and sweets!

The wheels on the bus...

The wheels on the bus go round and round,
Round and round, round and round.
The wheels on the bus go round and round,
All day long.

The Tweenies on the bus go chatter, chatter, chatter,
Chatter, chatter, chatter, chatter, chatter, chatter.
The Tweenies on the bus go chatter, chatter, chatter,
All day long.

Sit down and take a ride on the Tweenie Bus – where will it stop?
Do the actions too – first the wheels, then bounce up and down in
your seat, then chatter away and finally ring the bell – DING DING!

The bottoms on the bus go bounce, bounce, bounce,
Bounce, bounce, bounce, bounce, bounce, bounce.
The bottoms on the bus go bounce, bounce, bounce,
All day long.

The bell on the bus goes ding-a-ling-a-ling,
Ding-a-ling-a-ling, ding-a-ling-a-ling.
The bell on the bus goes ding-a-ling-a-ling,
All day long.

Bone zone!

News Time!

We've done lots of things in our annual! How much can you remember?

How many colours were there in Fizz's rainbow?

In the story about Betsy the snail, where did she finally decide to live?

Can you describe the big blue monster from the poem?

In the 'caterpillars and ladders' game, which did you go up and which did you go down?

How many bones was Doodles looking for in the 'bone zone'?

Have you seen my rain hat? I left it somewhere in the annual – can you spot it on any page? Have a look for it!

What happened to Incy Wincy Spider in the nursery rhyme?

Answers: There are 7 colours in Fizz's rainbow. Betsy decided to live in her shell. The big monster was big, blue and dripping with goo! Incy Wincy went up and down the spout. Down the caterpillars and up the ladders. Doodles was looking for 10 bones. Max's hat is on page 28!

59

Book chase

It's Story Time for the Tweenies. Throw a dice and hop from book to book. If you land on an open book, follow the instructions. The first player to reach the finish is the winner! What adventures will you go on?

Start

1

2 Stop to rescue Princess Bella in the tower! Miss a go.

3

4

5 Tell a short story about Princess Bella. Move on 4 spaces.

6

7

8 Jake is exploring in the jungle. Point to the tiger and have another go.

9

10